I REALLY want to SHOUT!

Simon Philip

Lucia Gaggiotti

templar
books

Sometimes I find it really tough
to make sure I'm not in a huff
because there's simply so much stuff . . .

. . . that makes me want to **shout.**

Why is it every single day
that just as I've gone out to play
my dinner's ready straight away?

That makes me want to shout!

If I want pud, why must I wait
until I've cleared my dinner plate
of green and yucky things I hate?

It's so **hard** not to **shout.**

And when I ask to stay up late
my parents won't cooperate,
which makes me get a bit irate.

I struggle not to **shout.**

But when I slam my bedroom door,
it doesn't help. We argue more.
I feel no better than before.

"It's **so unfair!**" I shout.

When morning comes, my mum and dad
need cheering up – they still look sad!
I try but fail. The mood is bad.

I think **they** want to shout.

So from now on I'm really keen
to be laid-back, relaxed, serene,
the calmest kid you've ever seen.

I'll never, **ever** shout.

Then in the playground at our school,
a selfish child does something cruel
and though I try to play it cool . . .

. . . I really want to shout!

And worst of all, he has no shame!
For when we're asked, "So, who's to blame?"
"It's her!" he meanly tries to claim.

I'm far too **shocked** to shout.

But then I suddenly unload
the silent rage I haven't showed.
I not-so-silently **explode.**

I try my best to stop and keep
my tears inside, but bawl and weep
a puddle . . . lake . . . a sea – it's deep!

I shout – and cry – **and shout.**

But luckily my best friend hears
and thankfully she soon appears,
by paddling through my flood of tears.

"Watch this!" I hear her shout . . .

And then she does a bellyflop,
which makes me laugh, my crying stop.
She's quite the expert with a mop.

"Incredible!" I shout.

And once she's checked that I'm okay,
she asks, "What makes you feel this way?"
"Just . . . **everything!**" I have to say.

"**I always** want to shout."

My friend then says, "My rage can make
my heartbeat race and body shake
so much I think that it might break.
I often need to shout.

But if I do, I have a rule
that helps me to regain my cool.
I draw my feelings. That's the tool
which helps when I could shout."

But when I next feel mad and stressed
and put her tactic to the test
my teacher's **not at all** impressed!

It makes **her** rant and shout!

I want to cry but try to hide
the way I feel and just decide
to bottle it all up inside . . .

. . . and hope that I won't shout.

But trapped inside me,
Anger glows.

He teases me, he
seethes and grows . . .

. . . until he's HUGE.
This monster knows . . .

I REALLY need to SHOUT !!

I fight the urge with **all** my might,
but later on at home that night
Dad sees that something isn't right . . .

. . . and lets me **scream** and **shout**.

He comforts me and holds me tight,
says, "Feeling angry's quite all right.
It's normal, so accept there might
be times you want to shout."

"I know just what you're going through,
as sometimes I feel angry too,
but let's work out what works for you,
so you won't need to shout.

Try thinking of your favourite place,
or find a calm, relaxing space.

Just leave when someone's in your face
and bound to make you shout.

Do share your feelings, make them known
before your anger's fully-blown . . .

. . . or write them down if you're alone . . .

. . . and feel like you might shout."

It's thanks to Dad I've found a blend
(a blend on which I now depend)
of clever ways to help me mend
my mood, when I could shout.

When I feel hurt and want to weep
I make my breathing slow and deep.

Sometimes I even fall asleep!

That helps me not to shout.

And when I want to scream and kick,
I've found that talking does the trick.
It really helps – results are quick!

I hardly **ever** shout!

Sometimes the only thing to do
is bounce just like a kangaroo
whilst playing songs on a kazoo.

It's too much **fun** to shout.

I find it stops me going mad
– could be the best idea I've had!
The only problem's Mum and Dad . . .

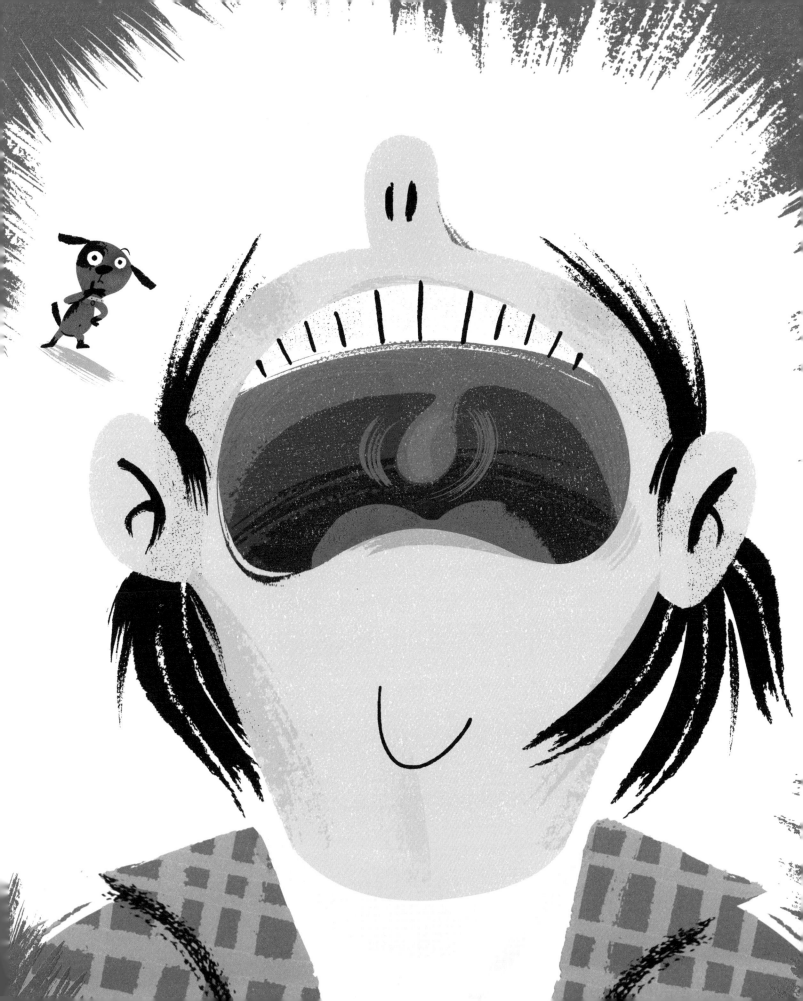

For Julie, Julian, Joe and Ben, with all my love x
SP

This book is dedicated to my inner child and that of my best friends,
Anja Roberta and Patrizia. Thank you for all your support!
LG

A TEMPLAR BOOK

First published in the UK in 2020 by Templar Books,
an imprint of Bonnier Books UK,
The Plaza, 535 King's Road, London, SW10 0SZ
Owned by Bonnier Books
Sveavägen 56, Stockholm, Sweden
www.templarco.co.uk
www.bonnierbooks.co.uk

1 3 5 7 9 10 8 6 4 2

ISBN 978-1-78741-680-2

This book was typeset in Brandon Grotesque
The illustrations were created with collage and digital medium

Edited by Katie Haworth
Designed by Genevieve Webster
Production Controller: Emma Kidd

Printed in Poland

MIX
Paper from
responsible sources
FSC® C018236
FSC
www.fsc.org

Colour in the monster if you REALLY want to shout!

Become friends with your MONSTER!